Non-verbal Reasoning

10 Minute Tests

8–9 years

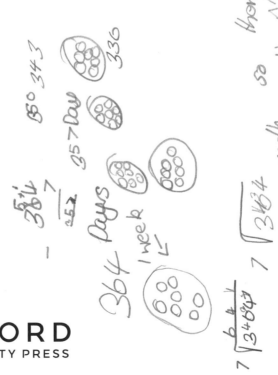

OXFORD
UNIVERSITY PRESS

TEST 1: Identifying Shapes

Which is the odd one out?

Example

Which picture or pattern completes the second pair in the same way as the first pair?

Example

6 is to as is to
a b c d e

7 Is to as is to
a b c d e

8 is to as is to
a b c d e

9 is to as is to
a b c d e

10 is to as is to

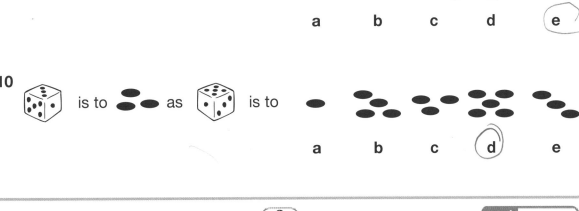

a b c d e

Total

Test time: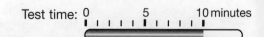

Which one comes next?

Example

1

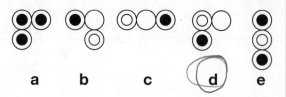

2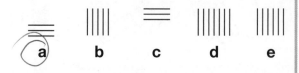

3

4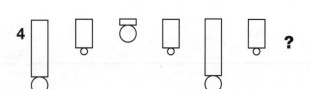

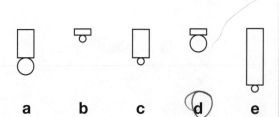

5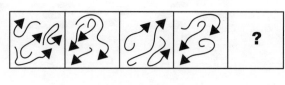

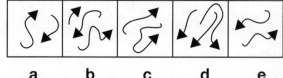

4

Which shape or picture completes the larger grid?

Example

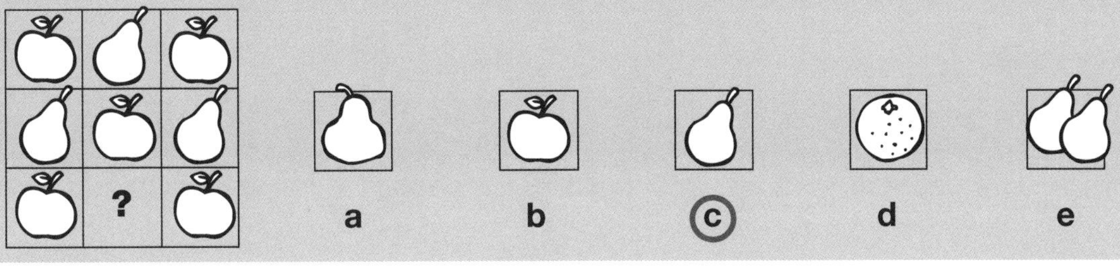

a   b   (c)   d   e

6

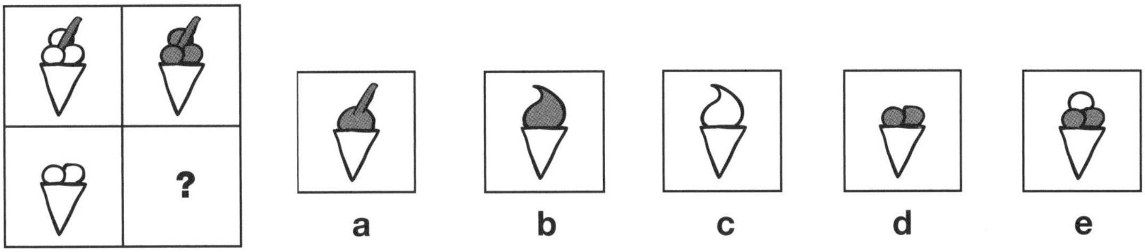

a   b   c   d   e

7

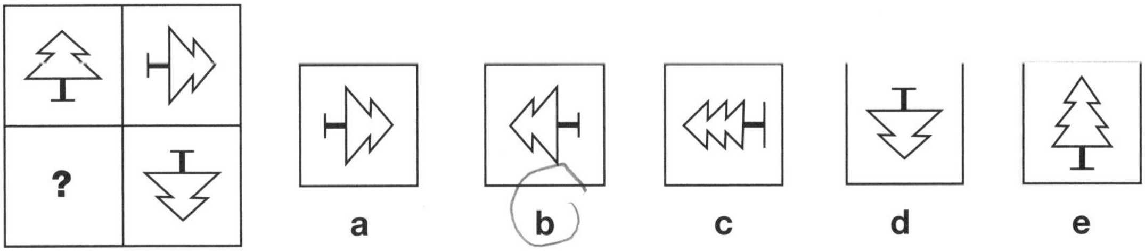

a   b   c   d   e

8

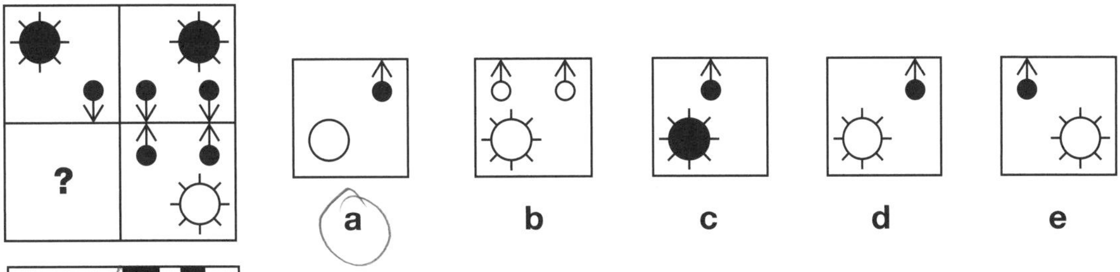

a   b   c   d   e

9

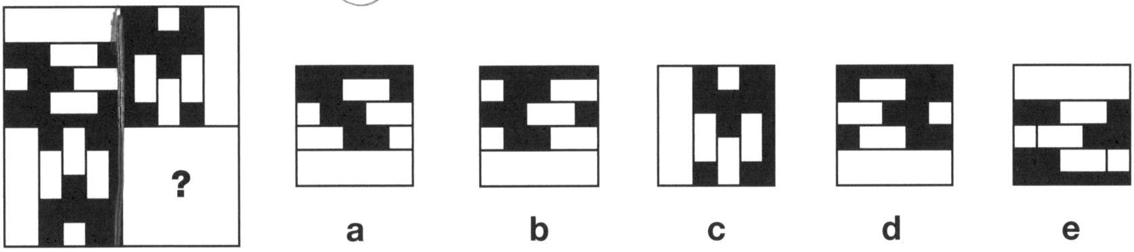

a   b   c   d   e

10

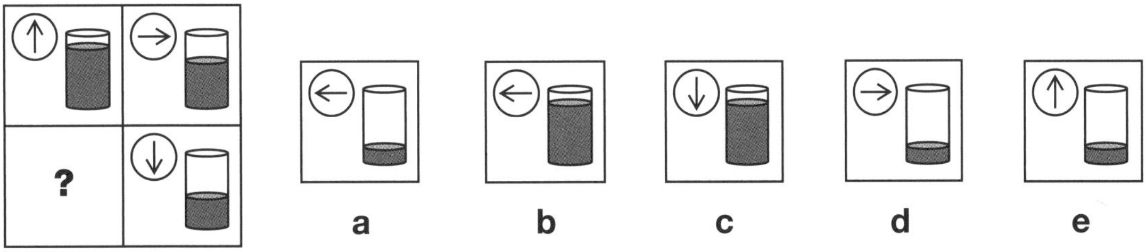

a   b   c   d   e

5

Total

Which is the odd one out?

Example

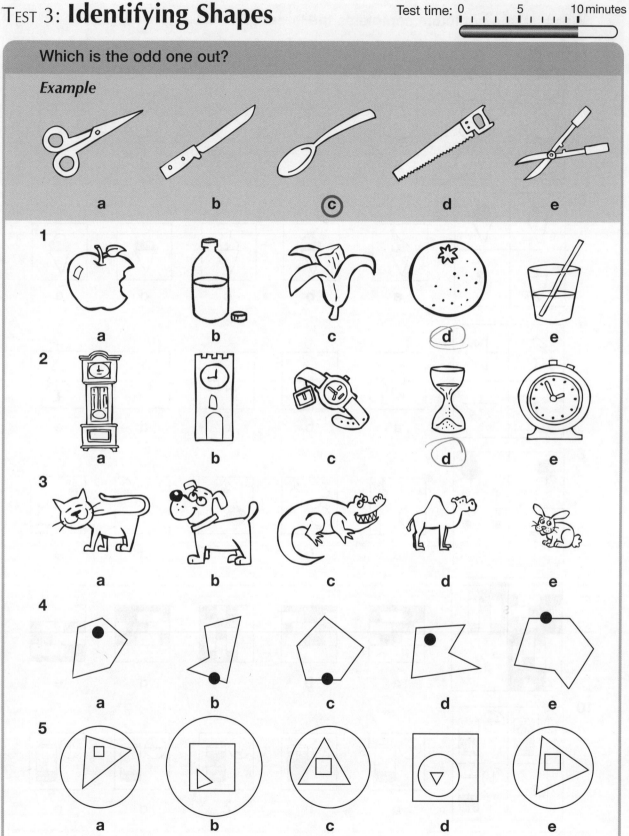

Example

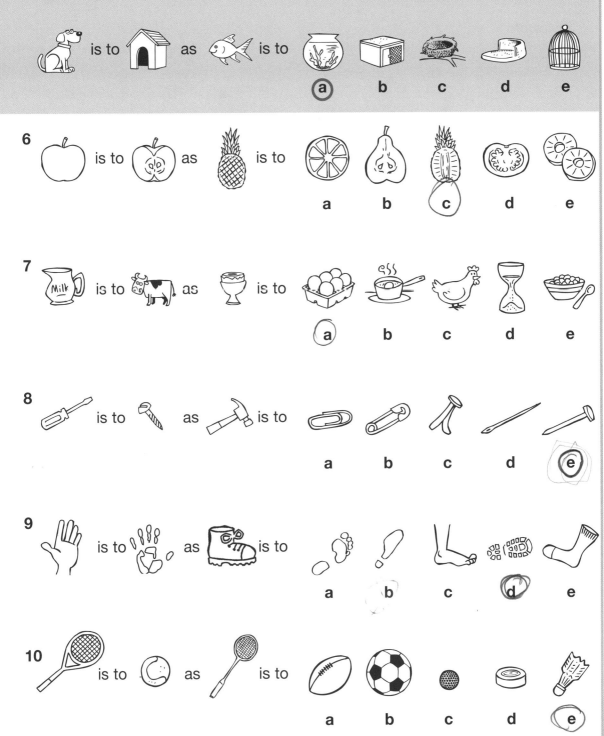

6

7

8

9

10

Total

Test time:

Which one comes next?

Example

1

2

3

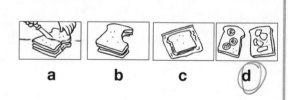

4

5

6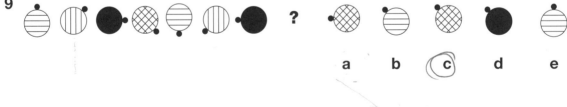

a   b   c   d   e

7

a   b   c   d   (e)

8

a   b   c   d   e

9

a   b   (c)   d   e

10

a   b   c   d   e

TEST 5: **Identifying Shapes**

Which is the odd one out?

Example

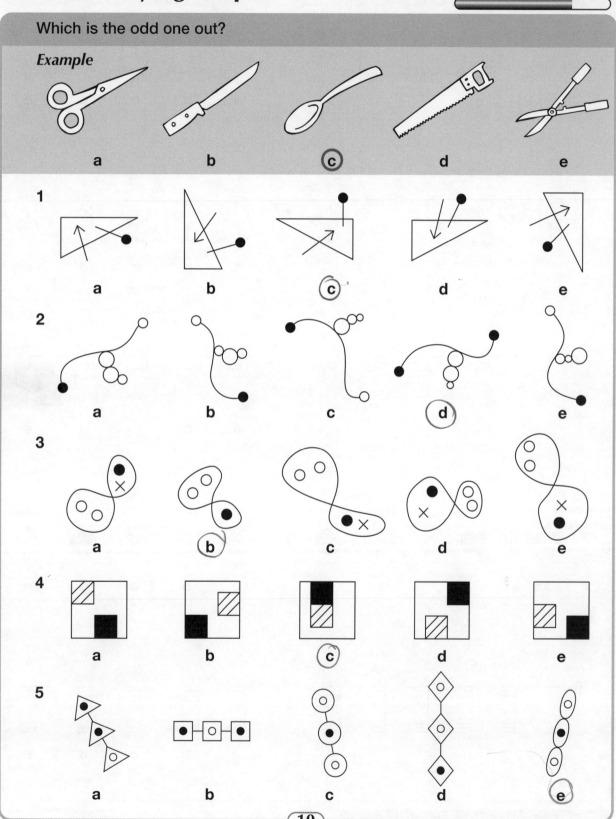

a   b   c   d   e

1

a   b   c   d   e

2

a   b   c   d   e

3

a   b   c   d   e

4

a   b   c   d   e

5

a   b   c   d   e

Which picture or pattern completes the second pair in the same way as the first pair?

Example

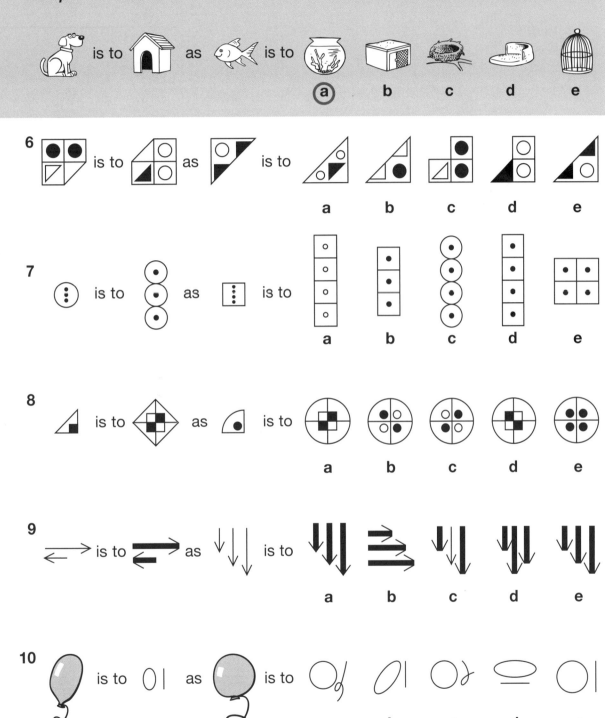

Total

Test time: 0 5 10 minutes

In which larger picture or shape is the smaller picture hidden?

Example

a b c d e

1 

a b c d e

2 

a b c d e

3 

a b c d e

4 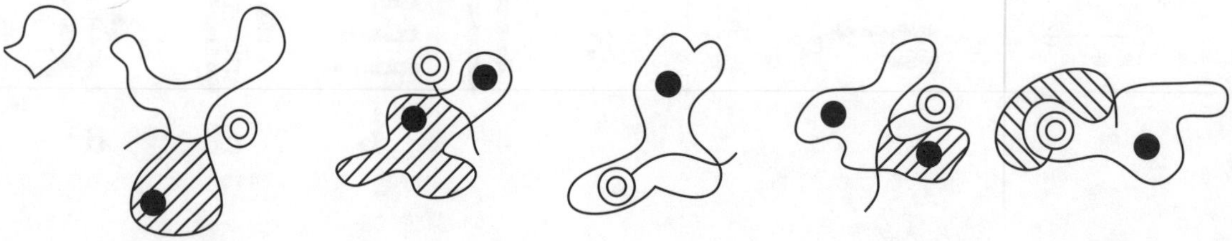

a b c d e

5 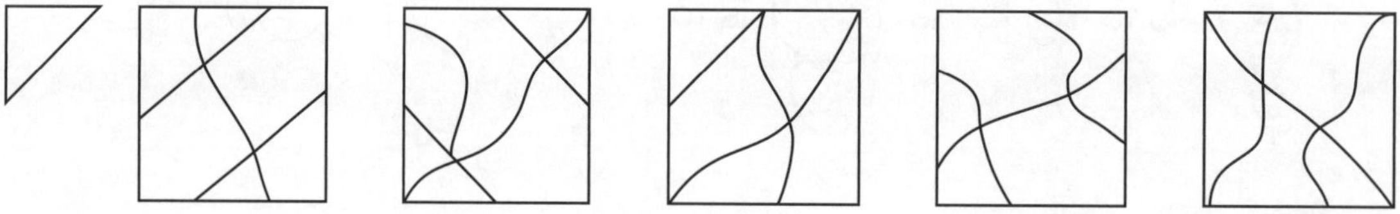

a b c d e

Which shape or picture completes the larger grid?

Example

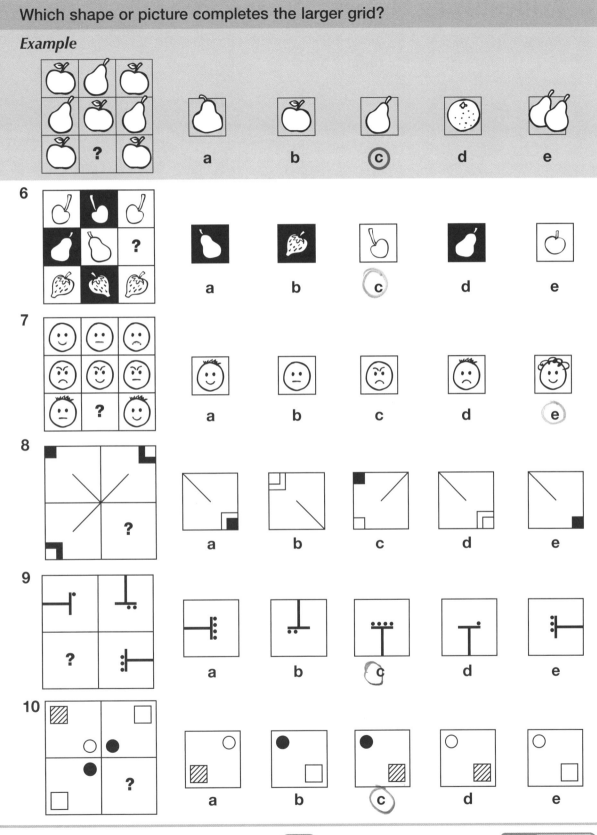

Total

Which is the odd one out?

Example

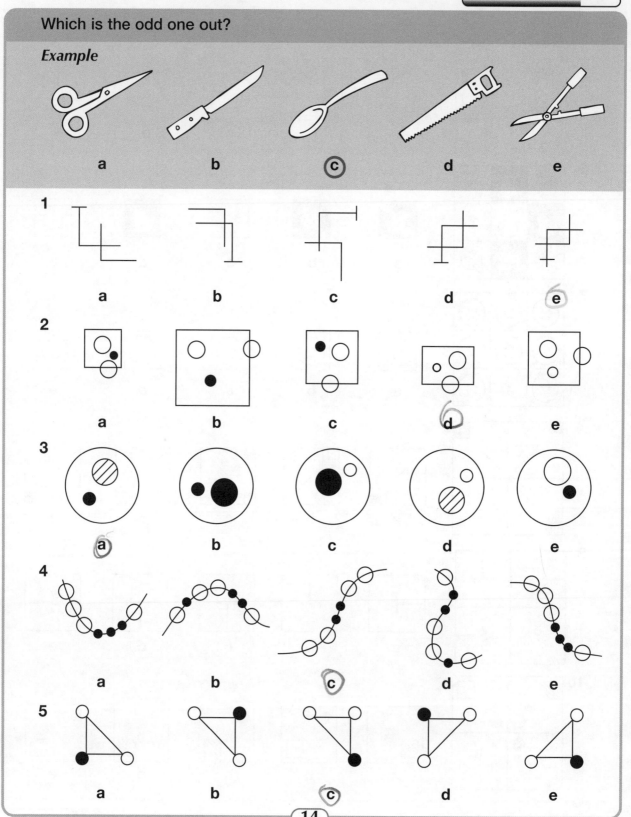

1

     a   b   c   d   e

2

     a   b   c   d   e

3

     a   b   c   d   e

4

     a   b   c   d   e

5

     a   b   c   d   e

14

Which picture or pattern completes the second pair in the same way as the first pair?

Example

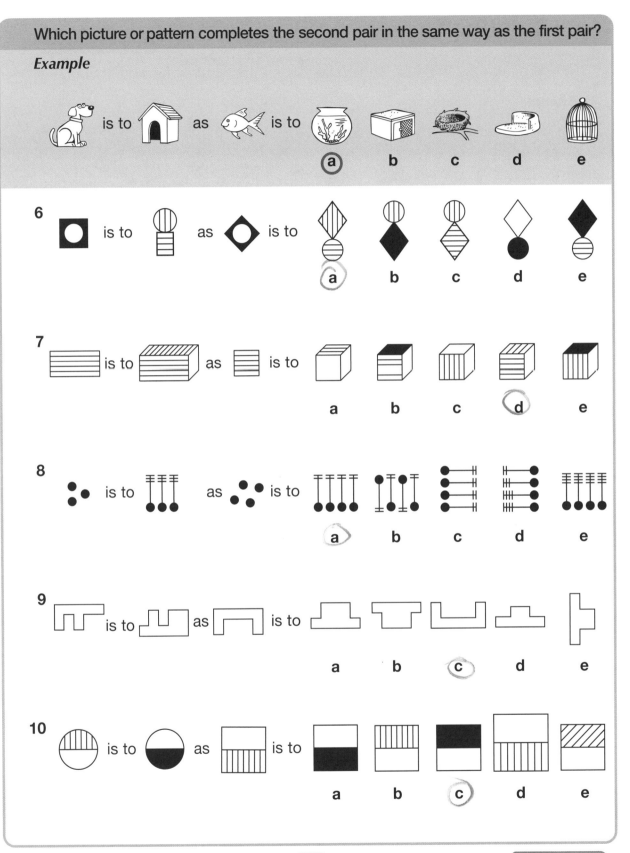

TEST 8: **Rotating Shapes**

Test time: 0 5 10 minutes

Which picture on the right is the reflection of the picture given on the left?

Example

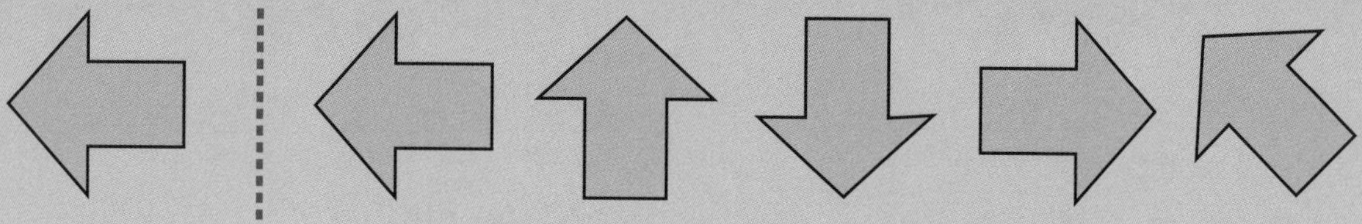

a b c d e

1

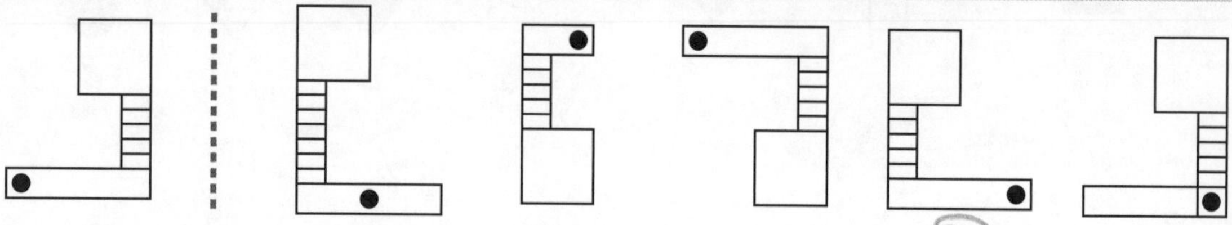

a b c d e

2

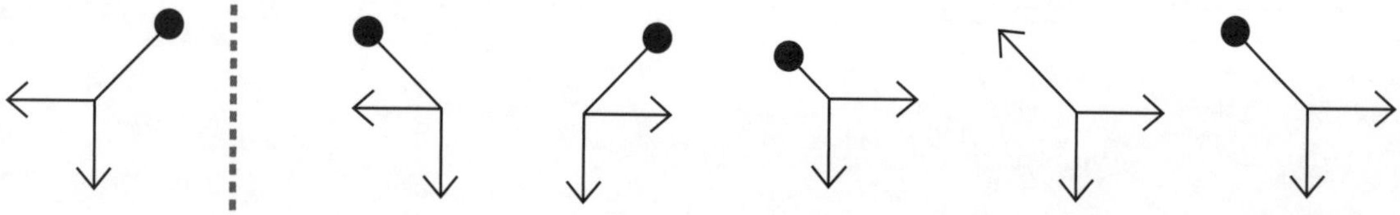

a b c d e

3

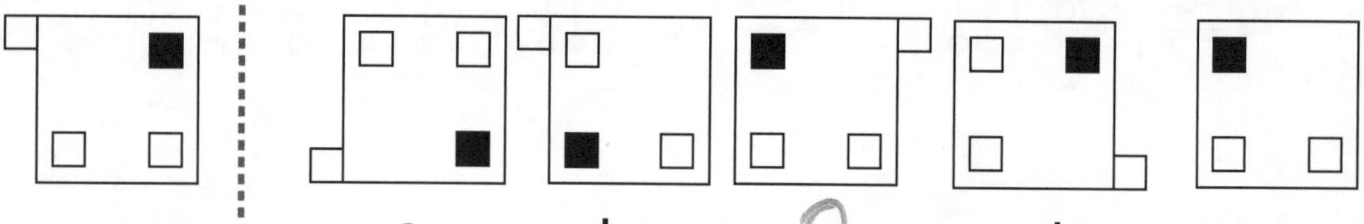

a b c d e

4

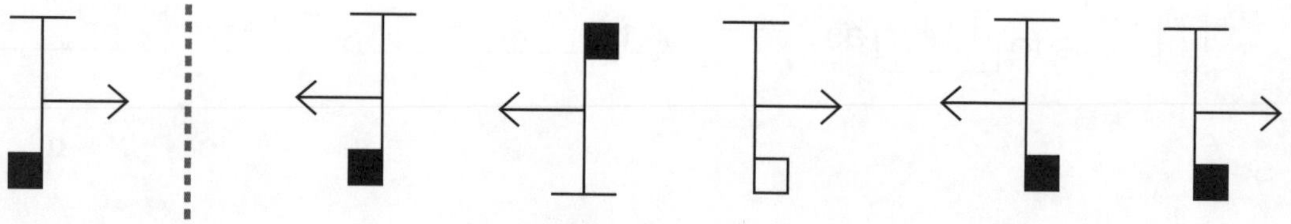

a b c d e

5

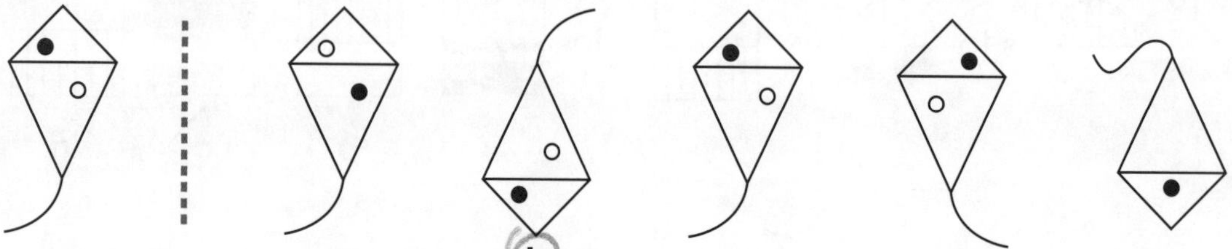

a b c d e

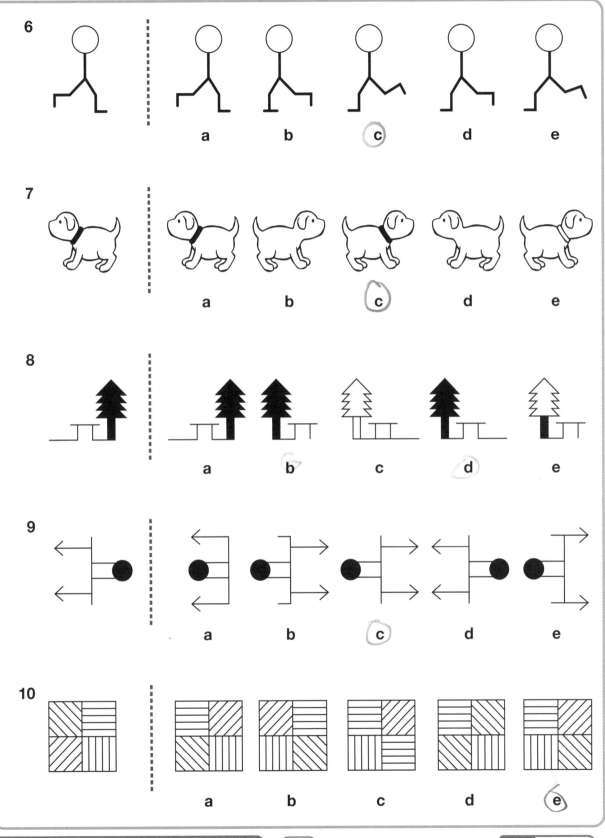

6

a   b   c   d   e

7

a   b   c   d   e

8

a   b   c   d   e

9

a   b   c   d   e

10

a   b   c   d   e

TEST 9: **Coded Shapes and Logic**

Test time: 0   5   10 minutes

Which code matches the shape or pattern given at the end of each line?

Example

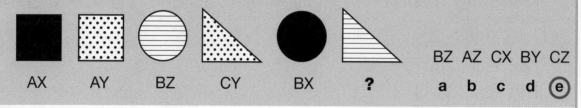

AX   AY   BZ   CY   BX   ?   BZ AZ CX BY CZ

a   b   c   d   (e)

1

XB   YA   ZC   YB   XC   ?   **ZB YA XA XC ZA**

a   (b)   c   d   e

2

CY   BX   AZ   AX   CZ   ?   BZ AY CX BY BX

a   b   c   d   e

3

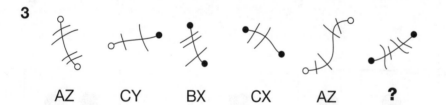

AZ   CY   BX   CX   AZ   ?   BZ CZ AX AY CX

a   b   c   d   e

4

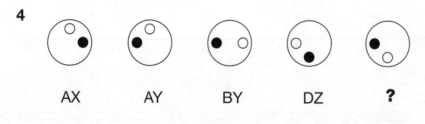

AX   AY   BY   DZ   ?   BX DY CY AZ CX

a   b   c   d   e

5

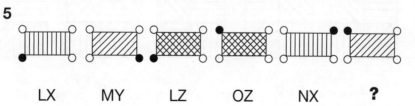

LX   MY   LZ   OZ   NX   ?   OX LY NY MZ OY

a   b   c   d   e

6

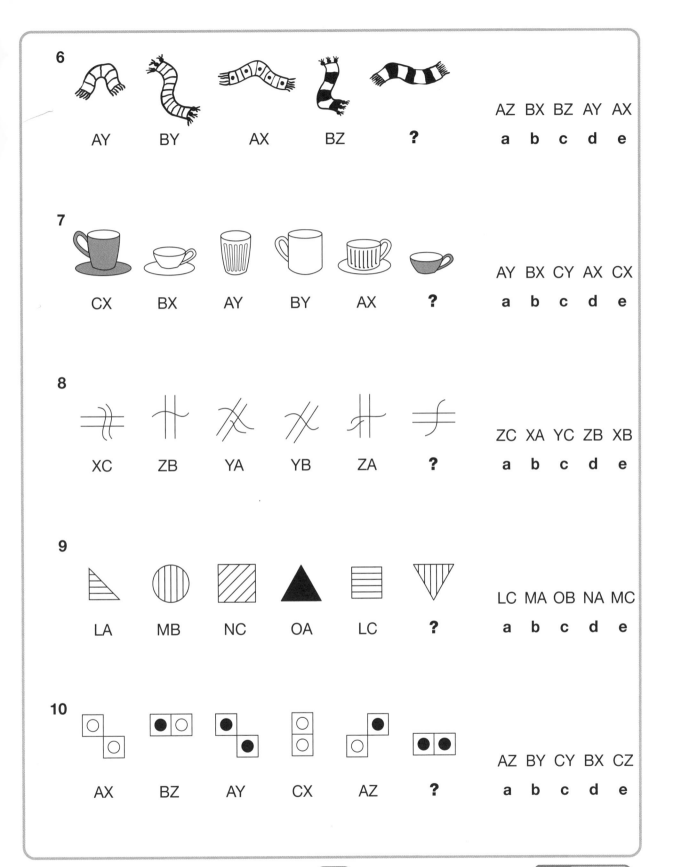

AY BY AX BZ ?

AZ BX BZ AY AX
a   b   c   d   e

7

CX BX AY BY AX ?

AY BX CY AX CX
a   b   c   d   e

8

XC ZB YA YB ZA ?

ZC XA YC ZB XB
a   b   c   d   e

9

LA MB NC OA LC ?

LC MA OB NA MC
a   b   c   d   e

10

AX BZ AY CX AZ ?

AZ BY CY BX CZ
a   b   c   d   e

Total

Which picture or pattern completes the second pair in the same way as the first pair?

1   a   b   c   d   e

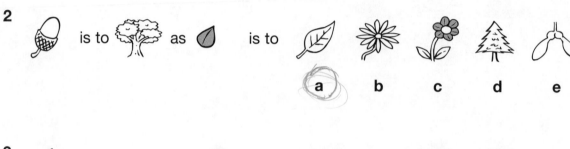

2   a   b   c   d   e

3   a   b   c   d   e

4   a   b   c   d   e

Which picture on the right is the reflection of the picture given on the left?

5   a   b   c ✓   d   e

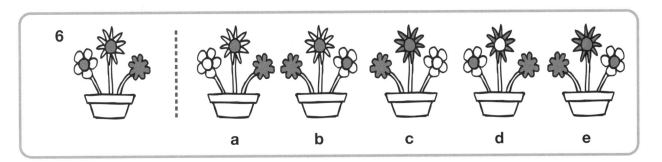

6

| a | b | c | d | e |

Which code matches the shape or pattern given at the end of each line?

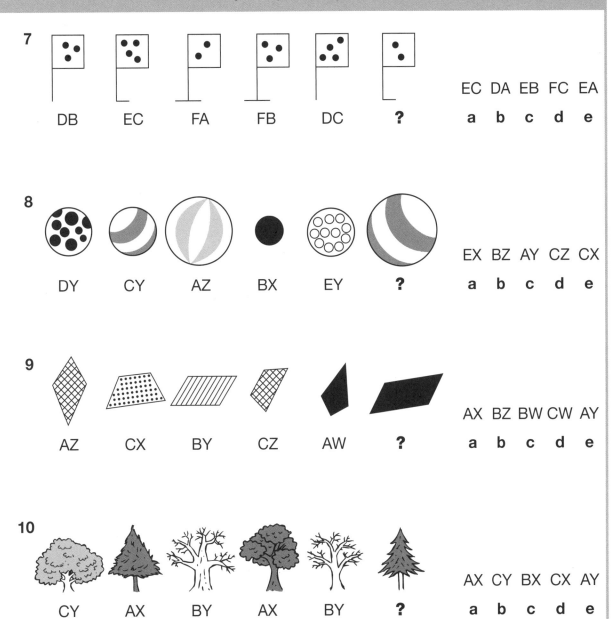

7

| DB | EC | FA | FB | DC | ? |

| | EC | DA | EB | FC | EA |
| | a | b | c | d | e |

8

| DY | CY | AZ | BX | EY | ? |

| | EX | BZ | AY | CZ | CX |
| | a | b | c | d | e |

9

| AZ | CX | BY | CZ | AW | ? |

| | AX | BZ | BW | CW | AY |
| | a | b | c | d | e |

10

| CY | AX | BY | AX | BY | ? |

| | AX | CY | BX | CX | AY |
| | a | b | c | d | e |

21

Total

Test time: 0   5   10 minutes

Which is the odd one out?

1

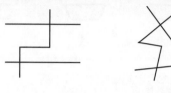

    a   **b**   **c**   **d**   **e**

2

    a   **b**   **c**   **d**   **e**

3

    a   **b**   **c**   **d**   **e**

4

    a   **b**   **c**   **d**   **e**

Which one comes next?

5

        ?

                                              a   **b**   **c**   **d**   **e**

Test 1: Identifying Shapes (pages 2–3)

1 **d** All of the table shapes apart from d have four legs.
2 **d** All of the leaf shapes apart from d have pairs of lines (veins) coming off the main central line; in d they alternate.
3 **b** All of the card shapes apart from b have the folded edge along a vertical side.
4 **c** All of the speech bubbles apart from c have five music notes.
5 **b** All of the butterfly shapes apart from b have the same colour body and head.
6 **a** The second picture of the pair is what is inside the object in the first picture.
7 **e** The second object of the pair is lit by the object in the first picture.
8 **c** The second object of the pair shows how the first object would be used.
9 **e** The second picture is the activity being done when the first object is worn on the feet.
10 **d** The second pattern has the same number of circles as the number shown on the top face of the dice.

Test 2: Missing Shapes (pages 4–5)

1 **d** The three circles in an L-shape alternate with three circles in a row. Each of the L-shapes has a white circle inside the circle at the corner of the pattern.
2 **e** Six vertical lines alternate with three horizontal lines.
3 **e** Squares alternate with triangles and the squares have a black spot alternating between the top left and bottom right corners.
4 **d** The middle-sized rectangles alternate with long or short rectangles in turn, with the circles at the end of the rectangles alternating between small and large.
5 **c** The arrowheads point to top right then bottom left and then the number of curly arrows reduces by one.
6 **d** The pattern in the bottom right is the same as in the bottom left but with shading the same as the grid square above it.
7 **b** From the top left square the pattern rotates by 90° (a quarter turn) clockwise moving round the grid in a clockwise direction.
8 **d** The pattern in the lower squares is a reflection of the pattern in the squares above, except the 'sun' shape is white.
9 **d** The pattern rotates by 90° (a quarter turn) clockwise each time moving round the grid in a clockwise direction.

10 **a** The circle with the arrow rotates by 90° (a quarter turn) each time moving clockwise round the grid; the height of shading in the cylinder decreases also moving clockwise round the grid from the top left square.

Test 3: Identifying Shapes (pages 6–7)

1 **d** All of the food and drinks apart from d have been 'started', they are incomplete.
2 **d** All of the objects apart from d have 'hands' to indicate the time.
3 **c** All of the animals apart from c have fur. Option c is also the only one showing its teeth.
4 **e** All of the shapes apart from e have five sides with a dot on one of the sides.
5 **d** All of the shapes apart from d have a circle as the largest outside shape.
6 **c** The second shape shows the inside of the first shape when cut in half vertically.
7 **c** The second item produces the first item.
8 **e** The first picture is the tool used with the second item.
9 **d** The second picture is the imprint made by the first object, for example, in sand or mud.
10 **e** The second picture is the object used with the racket in the first picture.

Test 4: Missing Shapes (pages 8–9)

1 **a** After getting a book from the library, the next action is to start reading it.
2 **b** On returning home from a hike, the next action is to open the door.
3 **d** The next action when making a sandwich is to put in the filling.
4 **b** The next action is for the girl to start playing, reading the music on the stand.
5 **e** The next action is to make the bread dough.
6 **d** The L-shape rotates clockwise by 90° (a quarter turn) each time and the black and white circles alternate.
7 **e** The three shapes in the sequence are repeated.
8 **e** There are two alternating sequences; in both sequences a line is added to the descending step pattern each time.
9 **c** The shading of the large circle has a repeating pattern of four styles and the outer small spot moves round clockwise by 45° (half of a quarter turn) each time.
10 **d** The short lines at the top start by decreasing then increase in number and the lines at the bottom start by increasing then decrease then will need to increase again.

Test 5: Identifying Shapes (pages 10–11)

1 **c** All of the shapes apart from c have the two short lines crossing the same side of the triangle.

2 **d** All of the shapes apart from d have one white circle and one black circle at the ends of the long, curved line.

3 **b** All of the shapes apart from b have a cross in the loop with the black circle.

4 **c** All of the patterns apart from c have the two inner shaded squares separate; in c they are joined.

5 **e** In all the patterns apart from e, the three shapes are linked by short straight lines.

6 **b** The second pattern is the first one rotated through 180° (a half turn) with the inner shaded shapes becoming white and the white ones shaded.

7 **d** The second pattern is the first pattern expanded with one black spot in each shape.

8 **c** The second shape is made up by repeating and rotating the first shape which forms the top right quarter of the new whole, with black and white shading alternating around the new whole shape.

9 **e** The second pattern is the arrows of the first pattern with wide lines and without sharply pointed arrow tips.

10 **e** The second pattern is made up of the shape of the 'balloon' pattern with a short vertical line to its right.

Test 6: Missing Shapes (pages 12–13)

1 **d** The right-angled triangle is only in picture d (as a wedge of cheese).

2 **c** The striped oval shape is only in pattern c (looks like a wrapped sweet).

3 **e** The small white bell shape is only in pattern e (the top flower on the flower stem).

4 **b** The irregular white shape is at the top of pattern b.

5 **c** The right-angled triangle is in the top left corner of pattern c. The triangle in shape a is too large.

6 **d** The shapes are the same in each row with the orientation and background shading alternating along the row. So, the shapes in the third column are the same as in the first column.

7 **d** The 'hair' and 'eyebrows' are the same along each row, with one 'smiling' mouth, one 'sad' mouth and one straight line in each row.

8 **e** The pattern in each square is a reflection of the square diagonally opposite in the grid.

9 **c** The top left square of the grid is rotated clockwise 90° (a quarter turn) moving round the grid in a clockwise direction and with one extra spot added at each turn.

10 **d** The pattern in each square is a reflection of the square diagonally opposite in the grid.

Test 7: Identifying Shapes (pages 14–15)

1 **e** All of the shapes apart from e have a short line on the end of one of the lines of one of the L-shapes.

2 **d** All of the patterns apart from d have a square; d has a rectangle.

3 **b** The two inner circles have different shading in all of the patterns apart from b.

4 **c** All of the patterns apart from c have three small black circles along the curved line.

5 **c** All of the patterns apart from c have the black circle on the corner that is a right angle.

6 **c** The second pattern has the inner shape of the first pattern on top, shaded with vertical lines, and the outer shape below. It has been stretched in the up–down direction and has horizontal line shading.

7 **d** The first shape becomes the front face of a 3D shape in the second part, with perpendicular line shading on the top face and a white face to the right.

8 **e** The second pattern has the same number of dots as the first, in a row, with a vertical line

pointing up from each and the same number of
small lines crossing at the top as there are dots.

9 **a** The second shape fits into the first shape to
make a rectangle.

10 **c** The second shape is the same as the first
but with the white section shaded black and the
line-shaded section becoming white.

Test 8: Rotating Shapes (pages 16–17)

1–10 To check and understand the answers for the
questions on identifying reflections, use a small
mirror: hold it vertically along the dotted line
so that the pattern is reflected in the mirror,
then you can see the pattern that is an exact
reflection of the given shape.

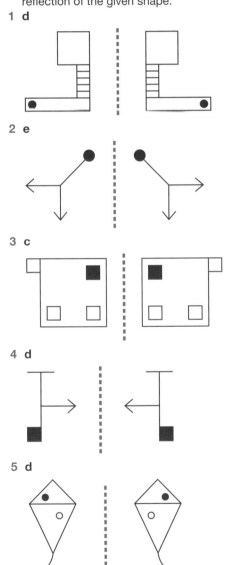

1 **d**

2 **e**

3 **c**

4 **d**

5 **d**

6 **d**

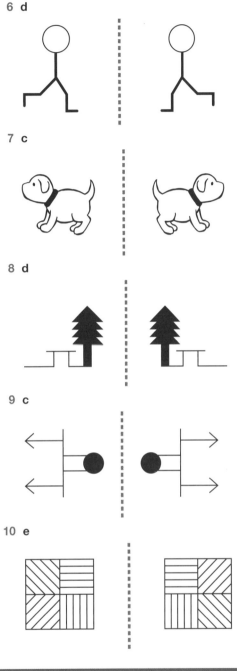

7 **c**

8 **d**

9 **c**

10 **e**

Test 9: Coded Shapes and Logic
(pages 18–19)

1 **e** The first letter represents the size and shape
of the parcel (X a cuboid, Y a small cube, Z a
large cube). The second letter represents the
style of 'string' around the parcel (A is plain, B
has a bow, C has a wide patterned ribbon and
bow).

2 **d** The first letter represents the style of tail (A is small, B is wide pointing up, C is narrow pointing up). The second letter represents the length of the beak (X is short, Y is medium, Z is long).

3 **c** The first letter represents the number of short lines crossing the longer curved line (A is 4, B is 3, C is 2). The second letter represents the shading of the small circles (X is both black, Y is one black and one white, Z is both white).

4 **c** The first letter represents the position of the small white circle (A is top of the large circle, B to the right, D to the left so, by deduction, C at the bottom). The second letter represents the position of the black circle (X to the right, Y to the left, Z to the bottom).

5 **e** The first letter represents the corner position of the black circle on the rectangle (L is bottom left, M is bottom right, O is top left, N is top right). The second letter represents the shading style in the rectangle (X is vertical lines, Y is diagonal lines, Z is cross hatched).

6 **a** The first letter represents the pattern of the 'fringe' at the end of each 'scarf' (A is regular, B is in groups). The second letter represents the shading along the 'scarf' (X has small spots, Y is plain, Z is black and white).

7 **c** The first letter represents the shading on the 'cup' (A is vertical pattern, B is white, C is grey). The second letter represents whether the 'cup' rests on a saucer (X on a saucer, Y no saucer).

8 **e** The first letter represents the orientation of the pair of parallel lines (X is horizontal, Y is diagonal, Z is vertical). The second letter represents the number of points where a curved line crosses one of the straight lines (A is 3, B is 2, C is 4).

9 **b** The first letter represents the style of shading (L is horizontal lines, M is vertical lines, N is diagonal lines, O is black). The second letter represents the shape (A is a triangle, B a circle, C a square).

10 **b** The first letter represents the positioning of the two squares (A diagonally touching at a corner, B adjacent horizontally, C adjacent vertically). The second letter represents the shading of the circles (X both white, Y both black, Z one white and one black).

Test 10: Mixed (pages 20–21)

1 **d** The second picture is a portion from the food in the first picture.

2 **c** The first picture is a small part of the object shown in the second picture.

3 **d** The second picture is the bottom piece of clothing of the person in the first picture.

4 **e** The second picture is the footwear worn by the person in the first picture.

5–6 To check and understand the answers for the questions on identifying reflections, use a small mirror: hold it vertically along the dotted line so that the pattern is reflected in the mirror, then you can see the pattern that is an exact reflection of the given shape.

5 **c**

6 **b**

7 **e** The first letter represents the line pattern below the square (D is a straight line, E is an L-shape, F is an upside-down T-shape). The second letter represents the number of spots in the square (A is 2, B is 3, C is 4).

8 **d** The first letter represents the pattern on the circle (A is curved lines from a point, B is black, C is shaded bands, D is black spots, E is white circles). The second letter represents the size of the outer circle (X is small, Y is medium, Z is large).

9 **c** The first letter represents the shape (A is a kite, B a parallelogram, C a trapezium). The second letter represents the style of shading (W is black, X is small dots, Y is diagonal lines, Z is cross-hatched).

10 **e** The first letter represents the top of the tree shape (A is dark grey, B is bare branches, C is light grey). The second letter represents the shading of the tree trunk (X is grey, Y is white).

Test 11: Mixed (pages 22–23)

1 **e** All of the shapes apart from e have two straight lines crossing the zig-zag line.

2 **d** All of the 'bone' shapes apart from d have a double curve shape at both ends.

3 **b** All of the candle shapes apart from b have a simple flame.

4 **e** All of the patterns apart from e have the square with the X in one of the corners.

5 **c** The spots in the large circles increase by one each time, the shading of the smaller circles alternates between the upper and lower half of the circle with black first, then lines.

6 **d** The number of black squares in each pattern increases by one along the sequence.

7 **d** The large triangle pointing down alternates with the three pointing up. The large triangle moves along the line from left to right and its central circle alternates between white and black.

8–10 To check and understand the answers for the questions on identifying reflections, use a small mirror: hold it vertically along the dotted line so that the pattern is reflected in the mirror, then you can see the pattern that is an exact reflection of the given shape.

8 **d**

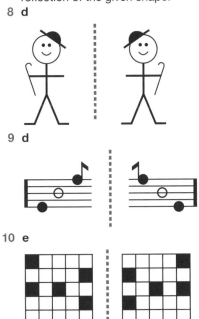

9 **d**

10 **e**

Test 12: Mixed (pages 24–25)

1 **e** The second pattern is the negative of the first, that is the black shaded areas become white and the white areas become black.

2 **b** The second pattern is the top half of the first pattern with the black shading replaced with vertical line shading.

3 **c** The second pattern is a large circle with sections shaded to match the number and shading of the small circles.

4 **e** The number of 'loops' in the first pattern equals the number of straight lines and crossing points in the second pattern.

5 **d** The repeating sequence is made up of four pictures.

6 **c** The beads on the top row move one at a time from left to right then all return to the left. When all on the top row are back, the first bead on the second row begins the sequence and then the top row repeats the sequence again as well.

7 **d** The circle alternates between black and white and the number of lines in the zig-zag pattern decreases by one each time.

8 **c**

9 **a**

10 **c**

Test 13: Mixed (pages 26–27)

1 **d** The object in the second picture is caught by the object in the first picture.

2 **e** The object in the second picture travels along the object in the first picture.

3 **a** The second picture is the result of the activity shown in the first picture.

4 **c** The next step in the sequence is for the sliced carrots to be served on a plate.

5 **d** The white circles alternate between plain or with a spot, the black oval is alternately below two circles then above two circles, and the circles are separated by black vertical lines, alternately one or two of them.

6 **e** Circles alternate with triangles; the shaded half circle moves round a quarter turn (90°) clockwise each time, the triangles alternate between pointing up or down with their shading remaining constant.

7 **d** Horizontal arrows alternate with vertical ones; the direction and shading of the horizontal arrows alternate and the direction and 'tail' pattern at the end of the vertical arrows alternate.

8 **d** The first letter represents the shading of the square (A is white, B has a X, C is black). The second letter represents the position of the black spot in relation to the square (W is to the

west/left, E is to the east/right, N is north/above, S is south/below).

9 **e** The first letter represents the shading of the larger circle (M is black, N is white). The second letter represents the number of small black circles around the edge of the shape (A is none, B is 1, C is 2, D is 3).

10 **b** The first letter represents the orientation of the curved line (L is a curved loop down, M is vertical, N is horizontal). The second letter represents the shading of the circles (A is all black, B is all white, C is black and white).

Test 14: Mixed (pages 28–29)

1 **d** None of the shapes apart from d have a right angle within them.

2 **e** All of the shapes apart from e have the black circle located outside the triangle.

3 **b** All of the shapes apart from b have a small rectangle at the base of the vertical line.

4 **c** The orientation of the curved lines alternates along the sequence, every third one has a black spot inside. On the other curves there is a white circle at one end, alternating between the left and the right hand end of the curve.

5 **d** The zig-zag pattern decreases by one section at the right end each time.

6 **a** The pattern of circle size is –medium–larger–medium–smaller–medium– etc. The larger and smaller circles are alternately black and white and all the middle sized circles black.

7 **b** Each row has two circles and all shapes in each row are the same shading.

8 **e** The pattern in the lower half of the large grid is the same as the pattern in the upper half. The correct option is also a reflection of the part of the pattern adjacent and to its left as well as a diagonal reflection within the bottom right quarter of the whole shape.

9 **c** The same shape in each column rotates 90° (a quarter turn) clockwise moving down the rows.

10 **d** The pattern of five shapes –black spot, white circle, X circle, black square, triangle– is repeated along each row progressing from left to right across the grid.

Test 15: Mixed (pages 30–31)

1 **c** The first object is placed within the second object.

2 **d** The first object is used to open the second object.

3 **c** The first image is the habitat of the animal in the second picture.

4 **a** The next stage in this sequence is to fix the saddle onto the horse.

5 **c** The arrow on the dial is progressively moving to the left.

6 **d**

7 **d**

8–10 To check and understand the answers for the questions on identifying reflections, use a small mirror: hold it vertically along the dotted line so that the pattern is reflected in the mirror, then you can see the pattern that is an exact reflection of the given shape.

8 **d**

9 **e**

10 **c**
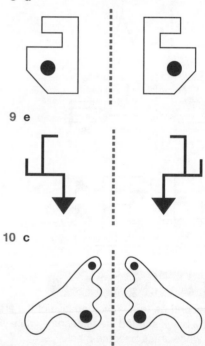

Test 16: Mixed (pages 32–33)

1 **e** All of the patterns apart from e are made up of three of the same shape.

2 **b** All of the shapes apart from b have a circle inside.

3 **d** All of the shapes apart from d have the straight line ending inside the central circle.

4 **b** The second shape is the first shape rotated through 180° (a half turn).

5 **d** The second shape is each part of the first shape stacked together and touching in the lower left corner of the largest shape.

6 **e** The second shape is the first shape rotated 90° (a quarter turn) clockwise with the diagonal lines removed.

7 **d** The shading of the square in the top left alternates between black and white and the spot at the bottom moves from left to middle to right, in a repeated pattern.

8 **e** The 'comma' shapes alternate in their orientation, reflecting in a vertical line, and the triangles alternate in orientation and shading.

9–10 To check and understand the answers for the questions on identifying reflections, use a small mirror: hold it vertically along the dotted line so that the pattern is reflected in the mirror, then you can see the pattern that is an exact reflection of the given shape.

9 **c**

10 **c**

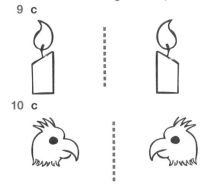

Test 17: Mixed (pages 34–35)

1 **c** The second shape is the outline of the first black shape without a base line.

2 **c** The second shape is the first shape rotated through 180° (a half turn) and with the small outer black shape changed to white and moved to inside the triangle.

3 **e** The second shape is the first shape rotated through 180° (a half turn) and with the short line moving from below the triangle to above the V-shape.

4 **d** The black spot moves progressively up the vertical line, swapping between pointing left and right.

5 **e** The number of black circles in the square increases by one each time.

6 **d** At each step, the number of vertical lines decreases and the number of horizontal lines increases, and vice versa; there are always six lines in the pattern.

7 **e** The number of sides decreases by one each time.

8 **c** The pattern along the bottom row is the same as that in the top row.

9 **e** The shapes in the top row are rotated through 180° (a half turn) to give the shapes in the middle row, and the shading of the shapes swaps between black and white down each column.

10 **b** The pattern in the bottom row of the grid is the reverse of that in the top row.

Test 18: Mixed (pages 36–37)

1 **e** The row of circles increases by one each time, until there are three circles then a new row starts. Imagine the circles are pushed in from the left each time. They are added in the order –black–white with spot–black– in each row.

2 **c** The number of black circles decreases by one each time as the number of white circles increases; the number of short lines crossing the curved line increases by one each time.

3 **d** This is a repeating pattern of four shapes: half-shaded circle, half-shaded square, white triangle, half-shaded triangle.

4 **e** The black horizontal bar moves progressively down the rectangle from the top; the shading of the rectangle at the bottom alternates between black and striped.

5 **d** There is one of each item in each row (and each column); none are shaded black.

6 **e** The same pattern is repeated to form diagonal lines across the grid from top left to bottom right.

7 **c** The pattern of shading in the top half of the grid is repeated in the lower half. Also, each row has one of each of the shading patterns.

8 **e** The first letter represents the pattern on the front face of the cube (A is a heart, B a white circle, C black). The second letter represents the shading style on the side face of the cube (L is black, M lines, N a black circle).

9 **d** The first letter represents the type of rectangle (D is large, E is narrow, F is a square). The second letter represents the shading of the circles (X is all white, Y is all black, Z is 2 black and 2 white).

10 **e** The first letter represents the number of loops on the outer curved line (L is 3, M is 4, N is 5). The second letter represents the number of black spots (A is 1, B is 2, C is 3).

Puzzle 1 (page 38)

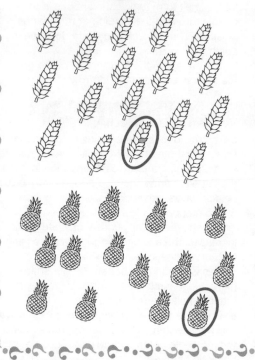

Puzzle 2 (page 39)

Puzzle 3 (page 40)

A 8	D 3	G 7
B 1	E 4	H 5
C 6	F 2	

Puzzle 4 (page 41)

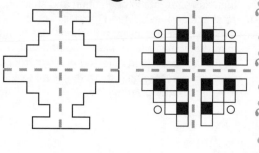

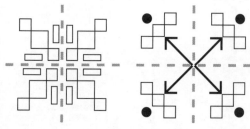

Puzzle 5 (page 42)

6

a   b   c   d   e

7  ?

a   b   c   d   e

Which picture on the right is the reflection of the picture given on the left?

8

a   b   c   d   e

9

a   b   c   d   e

10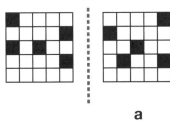

a   b   c   d   e

Total

Which picture or pattern completes the second pair in the same way as the first pair?

1 is to as is to

        a   b   c   d   e

2 is to as is to

        a   b   c   d   e

3  is to as is to

        a   b   c   d   e

4 is to as is to

        a   b   c   d   e

Which one comes next?

5

        a   b   c   d   e

24

6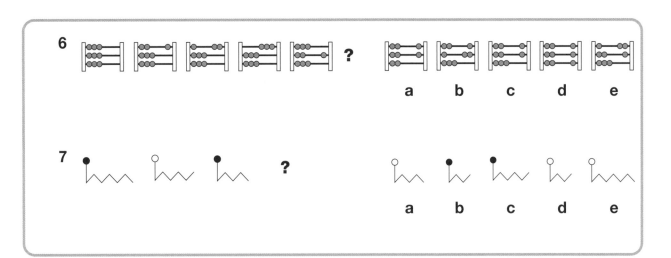

a   b   c   d   e

7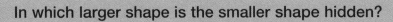

a   b   c   d   e

In which larger shape is the smaller shape hidden?

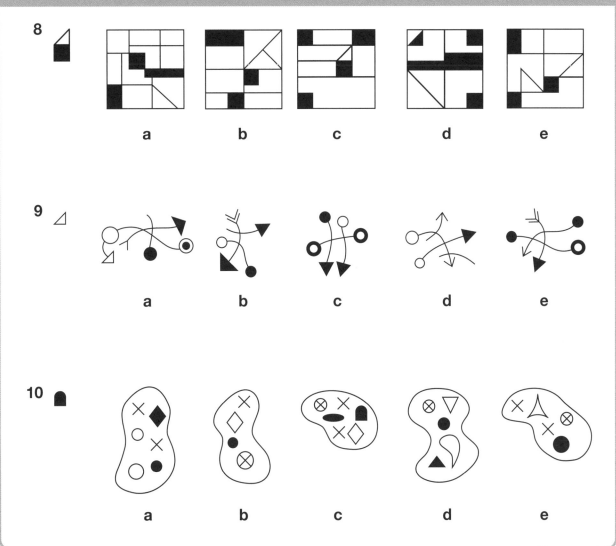

8

a   b   c   d   e

9

a   b   c   d   e

10

a   b   c   d   e

Time for a break! Go to Puzzle Page 40 ▸   (25)   Total ▭

TEST 13: **Mixed**

Test time: 0   5   10 minutes

Which picture or pattern completes the second pair in the same way as the first pair?

1

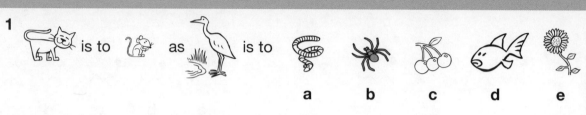

a   b   c   d   e

2

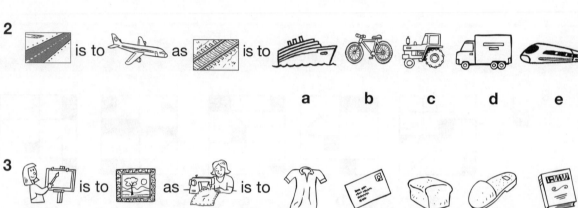

a   b   c   d   e

3

a   b   c   d   e

Which one comes next?

4

a   b   c   d   e

5

○ | ◯ || ◉ | ◯ || ◉ | ◯ || ?   ◯ | ◉   ◉ ||

a   b   c   d   e

6

                                              a   b   c   d   e

7

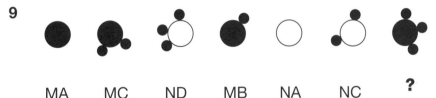

                                              a   b   c   d   e

---

Which code matches the shape or pattern given at the end of each line?

8

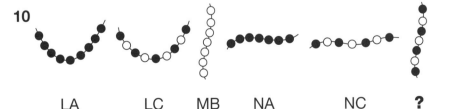

AW   BE   AN   CS   CE   ?

AS CN BW BN AE
a   b   c   d   e

9

MA   MC   ND   MB   NA   NC   ?

MC ND NA NC MD
a   b   c   d   e

10

LA   LC   MB   NA   NC   ?

LB MC NC LC MA
a   b   c   d   e

Total

Which is the odd one out?

1

    a   **b**   **c**   **d**   **e**

2

 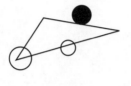

    a   **b**   **c**   **d**   **e**

3

    a   **b**   **c**   **d**   **e**

Which one comes next?

4

 **?**

                                            a   **b**   **c**   **d**   **e**

5

 **?**

                                            a   **b**   **c**   **d**   **e**

6 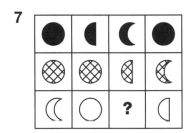 **?**

a   b   c   d   e

Which shape or picture completes the larger grid?

7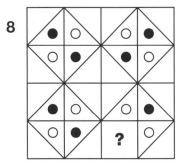

a   b   c   d   e

8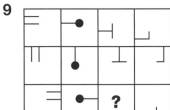

a   b   c   d   e

9

a   b   c   d   e

10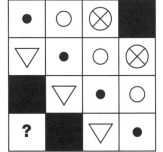

a   b   c   d   e

Total

Which picture or pattern completes the second pair in the same way as the first pair?

1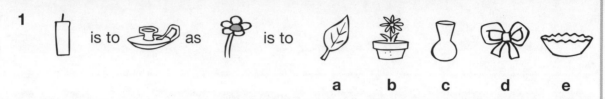

a   b   c   d   e

2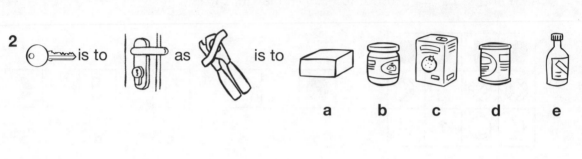

a   b   c   d   e

3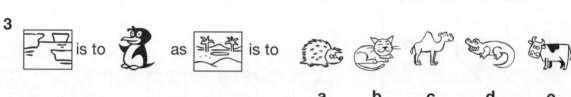

a   b   c   d   e

Which one comes next?

4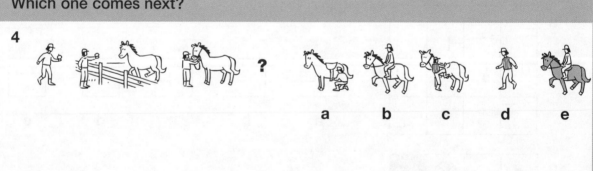

a   b   c   d   e

5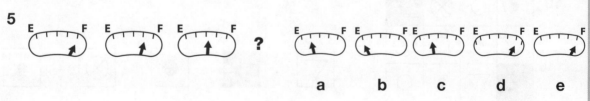

a   b   c   d   e

6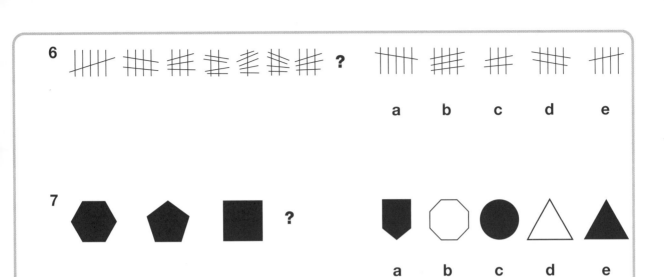

a   b   c   d   e

7

a   b   c   d   e

Which shape or picture completes the larger grid?

8

a   b   c   d   e

9

a   b   c   d   e

10

a   b   c   d   e

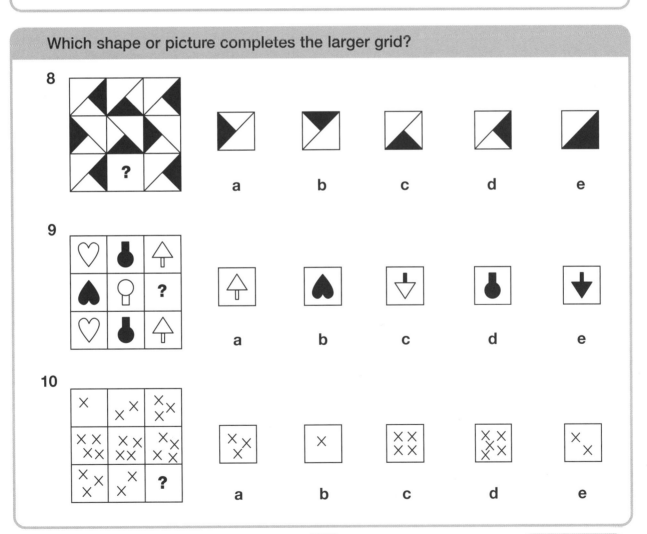

Total

Which one comes next?

1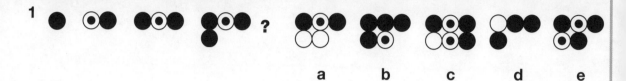

a   b   c   d   e

2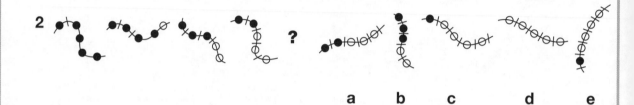

a   b   c   d   e

3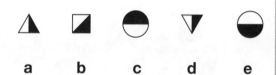

a   b   c   d   e

4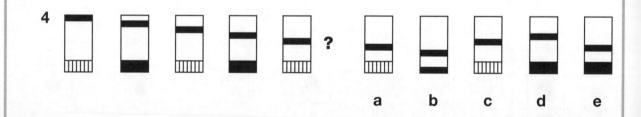

a   b   c   d   e

Which shape or picture completes the larger grid?

5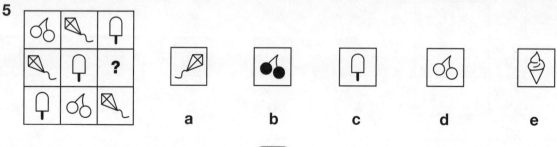

a   b   c   d   e

6

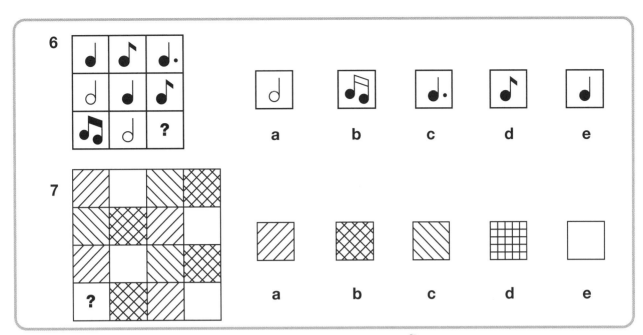

a   b   c   d   e

7

a   b   c   d   e

Which code matches the shape or pattern given at the end of each line?

8

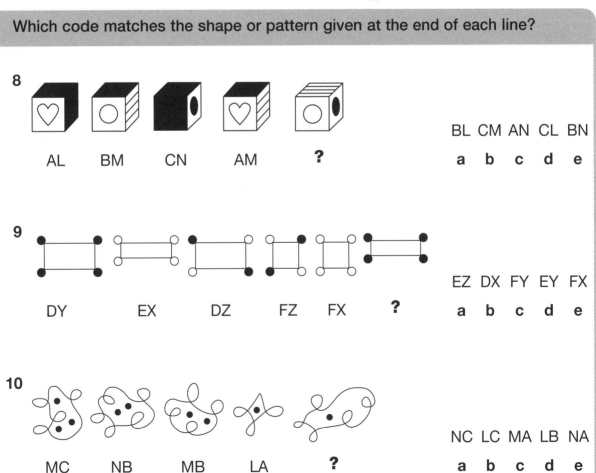

AL   BM   CN   AM   ?

BL CM AN CL BN
a   b   c   d   e

9

DY   EX   DZ   FZ   FX   ?

EZ DX FY EY FX
a   b   c   d   e

10

MC   NB   MB   LA   ?

NC LC MA LB NA
a   b   c   d   e

Time for a break! Go to Puzzle Page 42 ▶   Total

Puzzle ①

Draw a circle around the object that is different from the others.

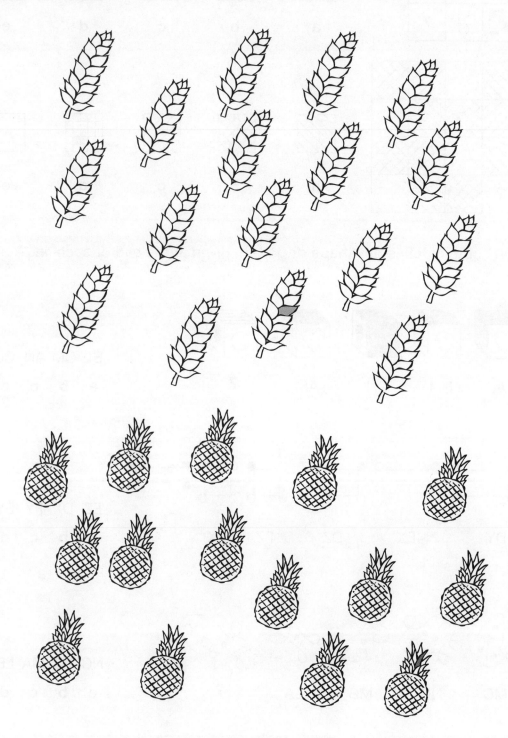

Puzzle ❷

Match the pattern to the shadow of its mirror image.

Puzzle ③

Match the missing squares to the letters given below.

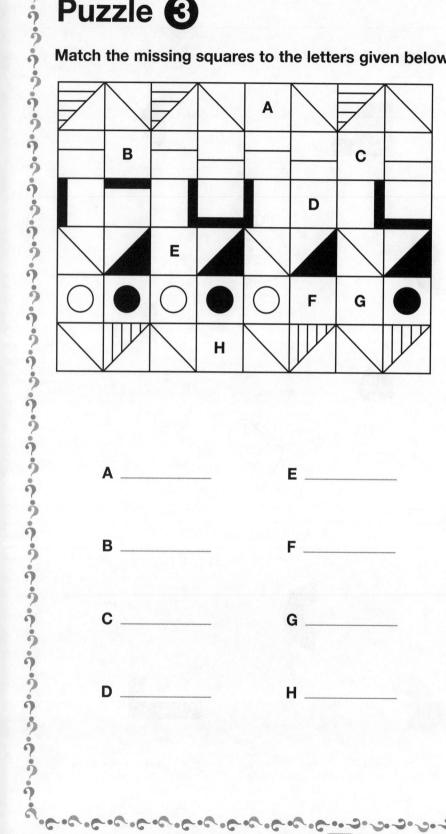

A _____   E _____

B _____   F _____

C _____   G _____

D _____   H _____

Puzzle ④

Complete these patterns.

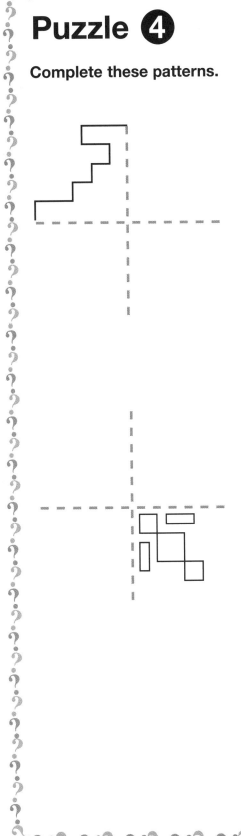

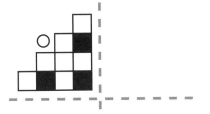

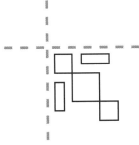

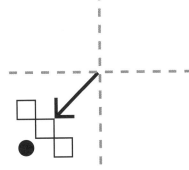

Puzzle ⑤

Where is this shape hidden in the picture?

Progress Grid _Non-verbal Reasoning 10 Minute Tests 8–9 years_

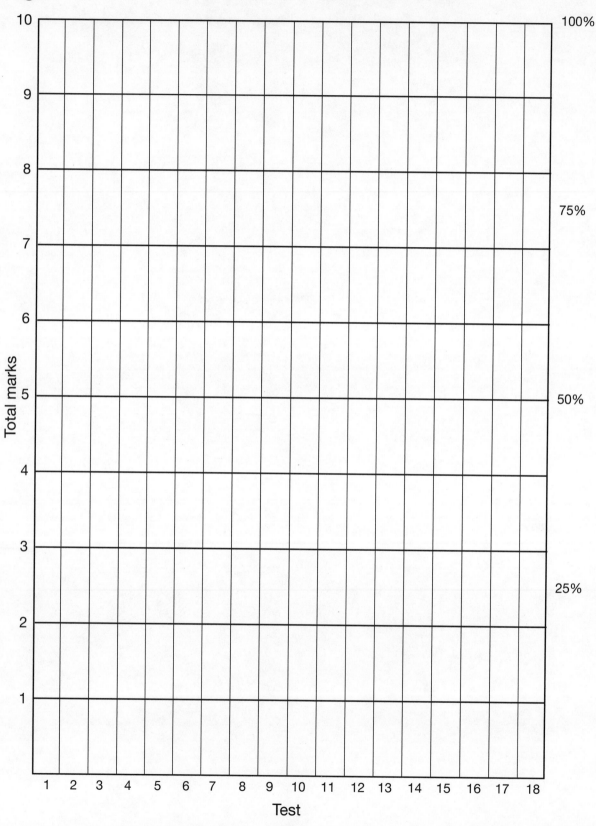

Total marks

Test